Acknowledgements

Half a Fish Supper and a Bar of Chocolate: Shortbread publications

Blue Moon, Snowdrops and Retail Intoxication Syndrome: Outskirts magazine

No' For the Likes O' Us: New Writing Dundee

A Window of Opportunity: Doris Gooderson prizewinner

The Woman Who Wrote Letters: Doris Gooderson shortlisted

Contents

Divorce Papers

In the mailbox, cramped amongst the flyers,
the two for one pizzas, cheap insurance offers
your flat roof repaired, a postcard or two,
Sits the stark white envelope from Court.

One sheet, a neat summary, factual,
Date and place of marriage.
Date and place of dissolution.

Nothing of the fun or misery.
I file the papers under F for Failure
But F is also for Freedom and Future.

I lay out three cards, unsigned
flat on the table top.
One says 'why?'
One says 'sorry'
One says 'go to hell'.

It would not matter which I send
All are valid, all irrelevant
I send none.

It is just someone I used to know.

Baggage

I searched out a place to leave it
The huge sackful weighted me
Impeding the journey.
A glittering snowy cleft high in Glen Doll
was too narrow.

By the periwinkled icecream prom
at Carnoustie, I sought spaces between rocks
But my arms failed to heft and lose it there
Where I'd danced free through foam.

Arbroath harbour pontoons bobbed, beckoned
But no - I heard that distant laughter.

I ran to Kirriemuir, looking
amidst squat red sandstone homes
for a grassy lane to dump it.

I lugged it down green blown mossy ways,
fringing Forfar Loch, I went inland again
past the magical house at Farnell.

I looked for the Brechin Picts
The sly, shy brown-clad ghosts
seen in the gloaming amid silver trees.
But they hid away from me.

At last, Montrose Basin shimmered
Endless sea met pellucid sky
Birds wheeled with cries in minor notes.

The rope tore at my hands, but I ripped
frenzied, till it fell away free,
releasing all upwards to oblivion.

The words, suppressed so long
were huge in my mouth
till they screamed away.

There were no tears.
The dying sun alone
watered my eyes,
and closed my throat.

Fox

I saw him that morning
Newly killed, slumped
In a paroxysm of pain
An old fox, grey-muzzled.
The hunter dead at last
The swifter rabbit fled.

A farmer later pulled him
Off dusty road, into the grass.

The man's hair is dim
Faded from childhood
To grizzled, balding tufts
Above haunted eyes.

Hunting, needing, he runs
Past oozing rubbish bins.
On grimy, garish streets
He meets men, grim on corners.

His predicted death
Now sure to happen
In slimy alleyway
Foetid, desperate flat
Or even clean hospital bed
Will not surprise either.

Food Banks

I stopped visiting skips
Once the food banks opened.
I trudged slick city streets
my sole adrift, letting in damp.
In sodium- lit darkness I slipped
behind Tesco, Aldi, Asda, Co-op
Climbing high, up and over metal rims
Stretching up, stretching down.
Easier to get things you don't need to cook
I have little money for the meter.

I saved the bus fare, walked home.
They get school dinners, thank God
But their pale faces, knobbly knees
Need supper too.

A councillor opened the food bank
Beaming ear to ear, fat, sleek, suited,
Snipping a yellow ribbon, speechifying.
Couldn't wait for him to go
So I could grab my bag of cornflakes
Tins of beans and soup.

That night, we feasted on tinned peaches,
condensed milk, biscuits, cocoa.

My children, flushed with sugar
Ran off to bed, replete, while I sat thinking
Feeling sick with shame.

The Waiting Room

It was the awful ordinariness of it all, he thought. My life is unravelling and everything around goes on as normal.

William Scott watched two women filing and answering the incessantly ringing phone from behind a blond wood reception desk. A little boy rolled a red ball across the waiting room floor, bowling over the little plastic dinosaurs he'd lined up in a row. The ball hit his foot and the mother, a frazzled, anxious-looking woman, told him off sharply. The child looked up at William and smiled, gap-toothed, his huge brown eyes meeting the man's for a second.

"Who is his dad?" William wondered. The mum had a faint white line on her left hand ring finger. Divorced, William thought. A harassed woman worried about money, probably. She had rushed in with the boy, late for her appointment and was now having to wait a turn to see the doctor. All so mundane.

Further along the row, a woman, in her thirties, immaculate in a business suit, was gazing blankly at the leaflets and magazines on the table, twisting a piece of paper in her hand, her pale lips moving faintly to her inner dialogue.

"When that doctor calls me in, I'll know for sure that Wendy had cheated on me and that the child she is carrying isn't mine", thought William. "If only I'd been honest with her at the start, and told her that my sperm count was so low that I was highly unlikely to father a child, I wouldn't be going through this torment."

His restless inner dialogue rolled on. "Macho pride, that's all it was when Jennifer couldn't conceive all those years ago and the tests showed it was down to me. And now this awful thing, Wendy's pregnancy. What the hell am I going to do?"

Fiona Brown looked vaguely around the busy waiting room, smoothing down her skirt and crossing her elegant legs. Preoccupied, she was aware of the heap of garish magazines and the spindly, untended pot plants but her attention kept returning to the crumpled bit of paper in her hand.

If Dr Robertson confirms the pregnancy, she thought, I'm going to propose to James tonight. She' been trying long enough to conceive and only the odd spasm of guilt flitted through her as she remembered assuring James, only a few weeks ago, that she was still safely on the pill. Would he make the commitment leap she needed, and do the nappies and bottles thing, she wondered? A movement caught Fiona's eye and she watched the small child retrieve his ball from underneath the chair of a pale-faced young man.

"That man looks like he has the cares of the world on his shoulders," thought Fiona, as she watched his expression first soften in a smile and almost as swiftly, fade into a strange expression of the most poignant sadness. Fiona looked away, and glanced down yet again at the piece of paper with the list she'd written: stability, a new life together, being a proper family, baby needing two parents.

Dr Robertson sat in his consulting room, his finger poised over the buzzer. He hesitated, and once more pulled up on screen the notes for the next two patients. He ran his hands through his hair in an impatient gesture which he'd first developed as a medical student when encountering particularly tricky passages in his text books.

William Scott's notes on screen in front of him contained the result of sperm tests. They showed conclusively that William could not realistically have fathered the child his wife Wendy was carrying - the wife who was also his patient. A DNA test after the baby was born would simply confirm the position. The doctor sighed deeply.

The other notes, marked Fiona Brown, were about to give him an equally difficult session. Far from confirming a pregnancy, the test results showed clearly that Fiona had entered an early menopause and her chances of becoming a mother were non-existent.

Outside the door, in the waiting room, the patients fidgeted and stared into space. The small boy painstakingly set up his row of garishly coloured dinosaurs again, and knocked them down once more with the ball.

Finally, Dr Robertson pressed the tannoy button and called in William Scott.

Lump-ectomy

Sounds harmless
Lump chump thump bump
Childish playground words
Scraped knees, Elastoplast
No threats there

Ectomy
Sounds funny
A garden herb maybe

Chemo
A music rap
Like garage grunge hip hop

Radio therapy
I like Radio 2, she thought
Terry Wogan till he retired
Johnnie Walker, Cilla playing sixties sounds.

Therapy, aromatherapy, candles
Hot white stones, fluffy towels.

This can be done, she thought
Gran gave her whole breast away,
That's not for me.

Cancer sidles crab-like
Sinister claws pluck at the edge
Finding a tiny crevice
Hooking into the lymph glands
Wading in the blood stream
Infiltrating, squeezing cells
Wheezing the lungs.

Her breath labours
Labour party, Labour day, labour pains
Words sounding serious now
Her hand can't lift to touch the nurse
Even though she is hard by.

Crab's wicked shell rises high
Triumphant, a fleeting, dying swell
As victor and vanquished perish.

The Spare Room

She glared at me from the spare room dresser
As I lugged my case onto the bed, uneasily
avoiding her reproachful gaze.

Rosemary. Limbs of rigid plastic, vacant eyed-
My sister's ancient precious doll, brought
from the attic to populate the room, she sits
with faded fans, dust laden doilies, lacquered vases

I felt Rosemary's bitter gaze follow me, relentlessly.
Mutilated in her knitted pastel dress and satin ribbons
her arms stretched forward, showing the ancient shame
where my small jealous scissors had snipped her fingertips.

Pulled from restless sleep by the baleful orange moon, flaring
through wind- moved muslin, I saw the doll had shifted -
a good six inches towards the dresser edge.
Her eyes glittered with vengeance.

Next night, I slept on the settee with the cat.

Flight

The swifts came back today
forked tails flickering
brittle black against clear skies.
free and clear they fly and swoop
nestbuilding with dusty wisps of straw.

They will raise chicks
in the fresh Angus air
swooping low at dusk, chattering
in wild ecstasy of freedom
battering over rain-soaked fields.

Come September's banking down
they will be called away
to Africa's mud baked huts
and pellucid blue air.

Like airline passengers
they will sleep on the wing.
Not pausing in flight
they will suck in an insect or two
sophorific, glazed with sleep.

I can only watch their flight
with envy and regret.

Half a Fish Supper and a Bar of Chocolate

The boy vomited into the gutter, his body jerking, shirt tail flapping loose, just as the Stagecoach bus rounded the tight corner into the bus station.

A man wearing an old -fashioned parka paused to light a cigarette under the orange lamplight, then neatly side stepped the boy, without a further glance.

"Good," I thought, rubbing the misted bus window for a last glimpse of the drunken, shivering boy. "I'll be right at home here."

One place is nearly as good as the other when your roots are so shallow, easily ripped up and replanted. Cities are best though, so you slot in, anonymous, no-one speaks, no-one asks. Though in fairness, Dundee looked promising, with the vomiting lad.

Every city has its parks and grand houses, where cheerful, successful people are seen washing their cars on Sundays. But cities all have patches of seediness too, where moss clings to ancient broken guttering above garish plastic -filled shops, and that's always where I end up living. I'm not complaining.

Yesterday I packed up my bags in the Kilmarnock flat, worked my last shift and bought a bus ticket north. Airdrie, Falkirk, Govan, Craigmillar. All the same, really. One supermarket's like another. People say there's no work but there is if you are prepared to take any crap checkout shifts for minimum wage, or clean toilets. I'll have a job by tomorrow night. Guaranteed.

I thought about the vomiting boy. I haven't ever been sick outside, except the once and that was special circumstances, in Edinburgh as it happens. The toilet in the Indian restaurant was in use and I didn't want to risk digesting the chicken korma, rice, naan bread and two puddings on the way home. I went up a close off Easter Road and did the usual. Felt bad about that, but, folk should make sure their entry systems work, that's all I can say, then I wouldn't have been able to get in.

That was the only time though, unless you count after the picnic with mum and Derek. I nipped behind a haystack and barfed, good as gold, they never knew.

Derek was probably the nicest one, he lasted longest. He called me chubby cheeks, though, which didn't help in the long run.

I've been everywhere, maybe I've always been looking for someone to share all this with, to understand. I've come close once or twice. In Kirkcaldy, my flatmate at the time, Wanda, nearly did it for me. She was wild, drinking and partying.

But then she found out about me, and couldn't hack it, couldn't understand the starving, the guilt , the vomiting and the guilt again.

One night she came round when I'd been in all day on my own, thinking about everything, and eating, eating, eating. I hadn't even made it to the toilet. I brought it all up in the kitchen sink and it was all mushy, clogging up the plughole. She came in just at the worst moment and her expression went from alarmed to disgusted faster than you can say carryout.

Odd really. She was often sick with drink.

I lifted down my case with the black strap and the old duffle bag and got off the bus, feeling in my pocket for the taxi fare. Always worth it, the first night.

The bus had only been £1, and even the juice, family sized bag of crisps and chocolate bars multi pack only came to £4. I picked a seat away from everyone so they wouldn't see me eating. It's always worse when I move, the nerves get me a bit.

Anyway, it was only a fiver for yet another new life, plus the 20p in the toilet at the bus station. Imagine charging! And I always make sure I leave everything spotless, too, so nobody can criticise me.

The taxi rolled along the night streets, past the Indian takeaways, the hamburger heaven, and the chippies. Pies, white puddings, vinegar scenting the air. Hating myself, knowing I'd be familiar with them all soon, I looked away.

The new flat was much like all the others: up a close, fairly grimy. Seventies kitchen and bathroom, showers with a mouldy curtain, a pine bed with a stained mattress.

I spent the next day cleaning.

"That's a side effect of the condition, this obsessive compulsive cleaning," the shrink told me once.

Good side effect, I thought. The man's an idiot to speak to me in that snotty tone of voice. Maybe he should keep his condescending manner for people who can't keep things clean and tidy.

By the next day, my kitchen shrieked of bleach, the toilet was pristine, toilet duck, brush, wipes all ready for action after the first meal. Only snag with bleach is if the rubber gloves roll down a bit, then the bleach can nip the scars on my arms. Strange how long they take to heal.

Started work the day after. Told you.

"What you doing tomorrow night , then? You fancy going for a drink?" The other check-out woman on my shift at the supermarket was hanging up her overalls in the staffroom and reaching for a fag and her lighter, ready for the first nicotine hit after six hours. I'd already worked out she was a dyke.

Trouble is that I look a tad Lesbian, which I'm not. Nothing against it on principle or in practice, come to that, but it just isn't me. Or is it? I might get too tangled up emotionally with a woman and there's enough to cope with already. Men are different, take or leave, generally speaking.

Or so I thought..

I turned and gave a half smile. My teeth are so shot to hell that my smile is Mona Lisa like, or more like a grimace, really, but that didn't put Josie off me.

"We could have a few wee voddies then a kebab and watch a dvd at mine if you like," she said, pulling on her coat.

She almost had me with the kebabs, but I stuck to the script.

"No, sorry, I've got a new bloke I'm keeping warm for tomorrow night," I said.

A lie, of course, but it did the trick.
Josie shrugged and went off out into the misty night.

I picked up my jacket and was just walking past the men's toilet when I heard retching. Force of habit made me wait and see who came out. George. Warehouseman, pasty faced, balding, moon- faced, but with kind eyes.

"You ok, mate?" I asked.

We went for a cup of tea, and I noticed that although he was untidily dressed, he had lots of coloured pens lined up neatly in his top pocket, and a folded Mars bar wrapper sticking out of his shirt pocket...

I thought, this is unusual. A rarity in a man, in fact.

"Don't jump the gun, Sharon," I told myself. "Take it easy. You know what's happened before."

But then I thought: my soul mate.

See, before Dundee, before George, there had always been this thing. It was like a huge, horse hair mattress, the old fashioned type with striped ticking, it sat between me and the world. I can see it clearly, and it swells up even bigger if anyone gets too close.

The mattress first materialised when dad didn't turn up that time at Christmas, when I had saved and saved my pocket money and bought him aftershave, even though he had a beard, I thought he would smell nice anyway.

Dad was going to come and take me out that day, after I'd had Christmas dinner with mum and, who was it? Bob I think, though maybe it was Brian. And we'd had all the turkey and everything, and the presents, and I had the aftershave all wrapped up for him. I was going to give him the present when we were on the big wheel at the winter shows, so he'd get surprise and pretend to drop it. Or maybe I would have waited till we were in the café having hot chocolate with marshmallows melting into them.

I hoped he was going to bring me a good present this year, seeing as how he'd missed last year and the year before. A CD player, maybe? Or roller blades?

When the phone rang I knew it was bad news. I listened at my bedroom door, staring at the parcel on my bed.

"Sharon will be so upset, you can't keep doing this Bill, it isn't fair," I heard my mother say.

Then she came through and gave me some garbage about his car breaking down and no garage open on Christmas Day.

I didn't even cry then, but I was grounded later that day for throwing the aftershave and breaking my dressing table mirror. And for eating two selection boxes, one after the other, and being sick on my duvet.

After that, the mattress was always there, lugged around from Greenock to Perth, Rutherglen to Coatbridge.

Until Dundee, that is.

All of that seems a long time ago now. Our cat, the stray George and I rescued, a thin and shivering little scrap, is four now. She's filled out, and is behind the front door yowling the minute she hears the key in the lock.

Last night, we had tea by the gas fire in our flat.

We were both rostered off work together for a change, and had been a walk up to the Observatory. Our feet crunched the dead leaves, all the way to the bus stop. Before we set off for home, we went to the McManus Gallery. Lovely chubby women in the paintings. George liked all the things about the history of Dundee: the old marmalade jars, and sepia photos of the buildings and people. His face broke into tiny crinkles as he chuckled at some of the old Beanos.

Coffee and one shortbread finger each in the café. No trip to the toilet.

When we got off the bus near the flat, it had turned raw and damp and dark, and the street lights were fuzzy orange. Couldn't wait to get inside.

We shared a fish supper and a bottle of juice, and had half a bar of chocolate each.

Then we cosied in together on the sofa and watched Strictly, and checked our lottery ticket. We didn't win, of course.

After, I went to make tea and as I passed the bathroom, I felt just this tiny flicker, just a faint, reluctant spasm, like the memory of a dream.

When I came back with the tea, George looked up at me over his specs and gave me such a nice smile, and we sat holding hands as we watched the news.

The mattress has shrunk to the size of a hanky.

Maybe this is what people call being happy.

Olly and Lola

In a heartbeat, in an instant, once more bound
By ties of blood and genes.

Daniel, Matthew, Adam, then Dylan, Osian
Locking me forever.

Now, two new people. A wonderous blessing
An astonishing bounty.

A darling boy, Olly, who nestles, sister safe
Calm, strong, knowing he's born into a good place.

A darling girl, Lola, with her brother, her other
Her smiling eyes scrutinise. She already knows her luck.

Two unique people, separate, but specially connected
Friends for life, never lonely.

The heartbeats in the womb set up a rhythm
Set to echo down through time.

The hospital said my heart was unremarkable
–their code for normal, healthy.

But my heart is remarkable
To hold such love for them all
To expand, fill, and yet not burst.

Talisman

In the first limmerings of love
Where each touch is fire
Every look a mighty tug within,
We saw the owls.

Mysterious, wise, beautiful
They watched us parade,
Click cameras, exclaim
All for their amusement.

Born from ancient myth
The secret midnight hunters
Sat stone still, sleepy
Scrutinising, sardonic.

The owls saw us together
Two quiet, glowing women.
Sisters? No, they knew.
Saw the burning.

I heard their message
In the echoed callings
'Have faith, it will be so'.
I listened, understood.

I bought the toy owl
So tiny, fluffy, cute
Unlike its fierce model.

A talisman for the future.

Rings

She wears her mother's ring, tight,
snug on swollen knuckle.
it slid from the old woman's wasted finger,
as slick as weeping.

The gold was rubbed and polished,
scoured by decades of dishwashing
and a corrosion of nappy powders.
Hands reddened and flaking, working hands.

In the bitter blackness of night the daughter looks up.
Glazed with grief, her teary eyes see midnight skies
littered and burdened with stars. Her mother lost
amid the billion distant pinpricks.

Daylight brings a comfort of clouds,
fluffy like those on childhood scraps where
cherubs rested, chin in hand, looking heavenwards.

Still her tears run, for the flawed memory
of an impossibly happy childhood
Glitter-eyed, she sighs, boils a kettle,
Her gaze lingers over condolence cards.

Another house, a different mourner, another ring:
The widower's face is translucent with grief,
He is hot and restless in the dark.

Night's pit holds him. Dreams find him
picking over the wretched debris of his life,
trying to find her, impossible.

The tie which choked him all day
loops black and cruel over the chair,
the dawn brings silhouetted despair.

His wife's ring cuts even his little finger.
He will wear it always now, with desperation.

Blue Moon

I was born once in a blue moon
Smoke rose high from forest fires on my day of birthing
Shrouding, obscuring the moon, turning its hue.

My mother watched from hospital window, bemused.
Her world changed, but the familiar skies altered too.

On the cusp tonight of another year
I pick green beans
grown lush in the crumbling earth.
In the gloaming, watched by stars,
I pull and snap nature's gifts.

The greenhouse glitters, vacant in the failing light
The hedges rustle with tiny mice and birds.
Wind chimes knock faintly, resonating
Reminding always of the first nights here, years ago
Their sound a harbinger of hope and content.

My last year here, bringing in crops
To store up, shoring against winter.
The beans will be eaten by others
Around a future dinner table.

A comfort of cats, a fire awaits within.
The moon stares down, as at the baby and her mother
All those years ago.

Once in a blue moon, if lucky,
We have a chance at true happiness
With a soul mate, another half, completion.

The trick, the real cleverness
Is to know when that chance is
and anchor it forever.

Roses

You came to me, suddenly
just as small rain fell here
on tangled flowers
clearing, cleansing the air.

You came from my city
where sodium lights stab
warm, noisy darkness.
From where my life began.

You came to me with roses
cut kindly, wrapped carefully.
their soft fragrance scented you
and swooned my heart

You came to me bearing faith,
tender trust and hope.
I opened my arms, enfolding
and letting you in.

A window of opportunity

It was a new shop, just near her office. She walked stiffly up from the bus stop one morning, the new bruise on her leg already blending darkly into the older one, still hurting. She noticed that the fast food shop was now open, selling pies and soup, thick sausage rolls, strong teas and chunks of garish cakes. Now she remembered vaguely, through the fog which seemed to cloud her brain nowadays, that men had been working there recently, hammering and sawing, converting the empty travel agency into a takeaway shop.

The day at work passed as usual. Pale, she blended into the background in her beige skirt and cardigan. When she first went back to work - it seemed so long ago- she had worn a red silk shirt and black patent shoes, dangly earrings, and swapped squirts of perfume with the other girls. They all used to go out at lunchtimes then, and have milky coffees and buns. Sometimes they went for drinks after work, and had cocktails with funny names and laughed and laughed, hardly able to hear each other speak because of the music and the buzz around them. But he didn't like her to wear anything nice to work, not even a smudge of lipstick .He said she just looked like a trampy tart, a dirty cow making up to men.

Homeward bound on the bus again, she felt the familiar knot of fear constricting her stomach. It tightened and gripped, intensifying as she opened the kitchen door. It was funny, this feeling. Like seasickness and bad period pains mixed together.

He was in, sitting smoking a roll-up cigarette and watching tv. Not watching really. His eyes didn't move to follow the programme: they were blank and glazed, but a tiny muscle in his cheek twitched. His whole body was tense as he turned his head , slowly, to look at her.

 Her heart sank: he was in a bad humour. There was an empty tin of beer on the floor at his feet, with a small spill of froth drying onto the carpet. David has his football training after school today. The thought dropped like a tiny weight in her head.

She turned to make the meal, picking potatoes out of the vegetable rack, beginning to peel them into chips, thinking of the cold ham and salad she would take out next. If we can get through half an hour, David will be home, it will be ok. David is nearly as tall as him now, though skinny, but he doesn't usually start anything if the boy's around.

His hand gripped her wrist, suddenly, startlingly. She hadn't even heard him padding through to the kitchen. "You're late, where have you been? And I said I didn't want chips any more, are you stupid as well as lazy?"

The blow to her face stung, but she ignored it. That was sometimes the best way, but tonight, her silence seemed to enrage him more.

She was dabbing her lip over the sink when David came in, muddy boots slung over his shoulder. His face seemed to cave in and crumble as he looked at her. Teenage boys don't like to cry, their faces just worked in a funny way. Their eyes locked for a second, but they didn't speak. He dropped his boots and went upstairs, quietly shutting his bedroom door with hideous care.

Next day, on the way to work, she reached the pie shop and stopped, looking in the window. Lots of different kinds of pies were there, on the new wooden racks: chicken and mushroom, ham, cheese, vegetarian, steak and onion. Each row of pies had a handwritten label describing the fillings. Vacant looking students, young office workers, hard-hatted building workers in fluorescent yellow vests stood in a silent queue waiting to buy sausage rolls and teas in plastic cups. £1 a pie, more or less. That would be £2 a day, plus maybe a few pence for vegetables and David could have a school dinner. Or they could have mince and potatoes, or some lentil soup, loads of vitamins in that. He needed to eat properly, he was still growing. But that would fill him up. She didn't need much at lunchtime, a few oatcakes, a cup of tea. She could phone the school to check about his dinners. And maybe the school would know about bus passes too, because wherever they went, he should stay at the same school. He needed to pass his exams, to have his friends, his football training. Normal things.

She lingered outside the shop for a few more minutes, just looking and thinking. A schoolboy waiting to be served drew idly on the steamy window. It all seemed possible, if she could just keep her head, keep her nerve.

In the office, she went to her metal locker with a key she took from her desk. It was still there, all of it, all the money she had saved, safe in the taped-up envelope. Not a huge amount, but enough for a deposit for a rented flat. She could go to the shops and buy plates and cups, sleeping bags, a kettle that would do them meantime. Each day now she would bring home things from the house, just the things she could carry in her shopping bag, and put them in the locker. A few clothes, photos of David as a baby, maybe the wee radio from the spare room.

Next week, on Friday, she'd meet David from his football training, and they wouldn't go back home at all. By that time, she'd have found them somewhere else to go.

And they'd have pies for tea.

The Zombies Play Carnegie Hall

Fourteen, walking fast and light
Through the town's night, from Guides,
My teenage angst at full throttle
Will he won't he will he ask me out?
Head filled with boys, clothes, Beatles
instead of French verbs and the future.

The music was faint, increasing.
Sodium lamps flickered orange.
I neared the hall
where schoolboys practised loud.

Haunting notes of the Zombies song
stood me still in the street.

The song charted on my blue plastic transistor
Forbidden pirate radio station muffled by my quilt.

Rod and Colin stared from my pinboard
The black and white photo carefully cut from Jackie.
So grown-up, sophisticated, appealing.
A mere five years older than me...

My hoarded pocket money bought the single.

Their music spurred my dancing feet,
opened a window in my head.

Half a century on, through and past working life
My children grown and gone.
Other sounds have rivered through my life.

In Dunfermline - at the other Carnegie Hall-
I see them live, smiling, wonderful
in touching space from these hands of mine
which have washed ten thousand dishes
changed miles of nappies, caressed lovers,
written a million words.

The boys of my youth are older
changed
but the same.

The middle-aged audience swayed in plush seats
with M&S bags, the odd walking stick at its feet,
as the thread of sound tugged back through time.

And we forgot our aches and pains
our reduced expectations, disappointments
and were all 14 again.

Snowdrops

This dawn, wrenched from a dream of loss
I saw weak winter sun glazing rooftops
Brightening the garden's Christmas cake frosting.

You were still here when I planted the snowdrops
Careful of the roots, pressing gently into the earth.
You watched from the old wicker chair, smiling.

I held the teacup steady, hearing
the reedy rise and fall of your breath
Faintly, a dying fall, you whispered

"Snowdrops, my favourites."

You touched my hand, as a million times before
Familiar with each knobbly knuckle, smooth nail.
Our roots twined, melded, stronger as two.

In the depths of this winter mourning
I remember the words, and see
The green spears piercing the snow shroud.

Topped with delicate white hoods
Tentative, afraid, courageous.
The snowdrops face the winter chill.

On the nearby brittle beech
The robin's song bursts through
Singing: "Love never dies."

No' For the Likes O' Us

It wisnae really like Ma tae swear, so Ah kent she wis really upset aboot the bairn. Then she went off her heid when Ah telt her aboot the other thing. Ah dinnae blame her in a way, it's jist too much for her tae cope wi'. I jist miss her, that's a'.

But see, it's when Ah look at ma bairn, ma wee lassie, Ah canny stop greetin' sometimes. It's like someone's turnt on a tap in ma heid, and the watter a' gushes oot ma e'en.
She's such a wee darlin', wi' yon big broon e'en, an' it jist disnae seem richt, somehow. Ah aye feel worse aboot it a' when Ah've been up at the hospital.

Ah've aye liked bairns. Ah liked lookin' efter ma wee brother and sister, takin' them tae the park, and up in the bus tae the toon near Christmas time tae see the lichts ad yon big tree . We'd go in the shops but Billy, the wee bugger, wid aye lose interest efter a wee while, and start muckin' aboot near the posh china, so we'd have tae go sharpish afore he hauled doon Edinburgh Crystal ontae the flair an' got us chucked oot.

Ma wee sister Charlene liked tae see a' the toys, though, yon big lot o' fluffy teddies an' cuddly big dugs wi' glittery collars. Her e'en went a' big and bright and she used tae go a' still, jist lookin' and' lookin' at a' they thoosands o' toys. Ah dinnae really ken why I used tae tak' her, for it aye made me that vexed that she couldnae hae any o' they things. "Tak me tae the shops," she'd say, though, every Christmas, an' Ah aye took them.

Ah aye winted ma ain hame. Ah used tae dream aboot it, an' imagine whit a proper hame wid be like. Some days Ah'd look oot the windae o' oor flat, fourteen flairs up in the sky, an' look at the bleak grey street. There'd be a burnt-oot car, like a drunk man lopsided, lolling against the kerb, rusty door hangin' off its hinges. The street wid swirl wi' scraps o' newspaper, an' crisp packets, an' there'd be laddies hangin' roond the Spar. They'd flick their fag ends onto the slimy street, an' spit onto the pavement, disgusting!

Auld folk, wearing trainers and scabby coats rich wifies frae the Perth Road gave tae the Oxfam shop, wid stand waitin' for the post office tae open. Ah aye think why should auld folk hae tae come oot in a' weathers tae get their wee bit money, an' have tae watch all they shutters bein' taen doon, like it was a fortress keepin' them oot?

Oor hoose wisnae up tae much, although ma did try her best. It wis hard tae keep oor claes clean wi' nae washin' machine, an' she didnae hae enough money tae get the food in that she wanted. It used tae mak' me laugh when they telt us at the skil aboot fresh fruit an' veg bein' gid for you. If you're livin' on Income Support, you buy chips and pies that fill up yir belly, never mind the broccoli.

Anyway, Ah used tae look oot the windae and think that ma dream hoose wid no' be set in a huge ,grim scheme where snotty-nosed bairns skipped skil tae sniff glue an' smoke fags they'd nicked frae the paper shop. Ah'll tell you aboot ma fantasy hoose in a minute. Ah can picture a' sorts o' details, an' ma ideal hame life widnae feature the polis liftin' the man o' the hoose at regular intervals, like whit happened wi' ma dad.
Ma dad wisnae even a success at bein' a villain - he aye got caught, whether he wis floggin' nicked Game Boys or breakin' intae hooses. Ma wid jist shrug her shooders when he wis awa' again, and then she'd get on wi' it.

But for someone like me, from whit they ca' 'deprived circumstances', Ah hiv whit Mrs Pearson ma auld English teacher caud 'a not insubstantial amount of grey matter' an' 'a fertile imagination'. Mrs Pearson wis dead nice, an' used tae lend me her ain books tae read.
"You should aim for university, Lisa," she said.
Ah' might as weel ha' aimed for the moon. Ma did go doon tae the skil yin day when Mrs Pearson wrote tae her, but she came back an' jist said: "Am sorry ma hen, there's jist nae way you kin stay on at the school, even with they grants she spoke aboot. Ah need ye tae work wi' yir da being awa'. Yon Mrs Pearson says yir guid at writing an' Ah ken that masel. But it's no' for the likes o' us."

So Ah worked in a shoe shop, an' got books frae the library. Ah fair liked that 'Sunset Song', ye ken yon auld book about the countryside up in Aberdeenshire, an' yon Chris Guthrie. It soonded jist great up there, an' Ah used tae dream aboot bein' a farmer's wife, wi' lots of lovely bairns, an' a' yon fresh, green countryside.

There'd be a cosy log fire, wi' breid bakin' in the oven. an' me sittin' knittin' o' a winter's nicht while me and ma man watched the tele, wi' the snow and wind batterin' the auld stone fairmhoose. I'd hae loads o' books, of course, an' ma bairns would a' be brainy an' good lookin'. Ah'd hae loads of nice freends in the cottages roond aboot, and Ah'd go tae concerts in the village

An' there'd be room in ma hoose for ma and ma brither an' sister, they could stay an' play oot in the fields or doon by the stream. It wid be dead healthy for them. Ma could sit an' watch the tele, or help me do few wee chores, nothin' too much, but jist a bit tae keep her hand in, like. An' that worried look wid go aff her face.

But a' o' that wis cloud cuckoo land, an' aboot as likely as me ga'en tae university.

Ah kent Rab- that's Jessie's dad- wis intae drugs an' a' that stuff when Ah first met him. Ye cannae live doon our bit withoot getting tae ken a' the bad lads- the druggies, boozers, car nickers an' the rest o' the dodgy yins. Ma said: "Keep awa' frae that yin, Lisa, he's bad news."
But whit are ye like at 16? He had a braw smile, afae white teeth an' dimples, wid' ye believe? He wis awfae cute, an' a great laugh-never a dull meenute wi' him around.
Ah' didnae like him shootin' up - grass or a few pills is yin thing, but the needle's somethin' else.
"Dinnae worry sae much aboot me," he'd say, an' gie' me a big sloppy kiss, then we'd gae'n oot for a cairryoot.

Ma was richt though. He jist didnae want tae ken aboot the bairn. When Ah' telt him ah wis up the stick, he jist bolted. Maybe he kent he wisnae weel by that time anyway, but Ah niver saw him for dust. Niver saw him again, full stop, unless you coont his funeral. Funny enough, he didnae die the way Ah thoucht he wid - he wis stabbed outside some pub yin nicht by a so-ca'd mate. it wis aboot drugs money- there's a surprise. There wis aye some bloke efter him.

Ah had the bairn, an' here we are in this cooncil flat in Whitfield - Ma didnae want tae ken aboot the bairn. She telt me: "A've enought tae dae withoot bringin' up your wee bastard an' a'. Christ knows there's no' enough tae go roond as it is."

She doesnae need any mair worries, Ah ken, but maybe ah wis just hopin' she wid hae helped me wi' everything. It's when Ah've had they nicht sweats an' ah wake up feelin' really crap, and scared. Ah wish Ma wis here wi' me, like when I wis wee and had a bad dream. She'd cuddle me up wi' her an' stroke ma' hair until Ah' calmed doon. 'You've got such bonny hair ma lamb,' she'd say, 'it's jist like silk.'

The doctor telt me yin day: "You've been really unlucky, Lisa, there's usually so much more we can do these days. But we think your pregnancy speeded things up and the drugs regimes we've tried don't seem to be working."

Whit wis Ah supposed tae say tae that? Yon doctor didnae look auld enough tae have tae be tellin' folk a' this bad stuff-he looked knackered an' a'. Yin bit o' ma brain wis thinkin' it must be crap for him an' a'. He must feel bad seein' a young lassie like me here. The only thing that is lucky is that the bairn is ok- but it fair twists ma guts tae look at her an' ken there's only ga'en tae be a few mair months thegither.

Last week, we got the bus and went doon tae Broughty Ferry. Ah pit her in yon buggy the social worker got me, an' Ah walked doon tae the beach, pointin' oot a' the shops an' cars and things tae her. She tried tae grab a wee broon dug sittin' outside a fruit shop, an' she swivelled richt roond watching it, as I pushed her doon the street, Then she spotted a massive bunch o' balloons tied up outside a wee newsagents, and made as if tae get them an' a.'

Ah boucht her a pink and silver yin wi' 'it's a girl' on it. It wis really for folk takin' tae the hospital for a new baby, but Ah thoucht, what the hell,we niver got balloons or flooers, or even a card, come tae think o' it, when she wis born. She can hae it noo.

We went richt doon ontae the beach. It wis freezin' cauld, wi' the wind blawin' intae oor faces. They seagulls made a hell o' a racket, but the bairn pit up her wee hands, tryin' tae grab them an' a'. Her wee mittens were half off, an' Ah cuddled her up close an' tight as Ah pit them back on again. "Silly Jessie, kept yir hands cosy!" Ah telt her, laughin' an' kissin' her wee cauld cheeks. She started laughin' an' a', an' pulled ma hair, then she said 'mum mum,' her first words.

Ah thoucht ma heirt was ga'en tae brak' richt there an' then on that beach, wi' the frothy waves crashing a few yards away. See, suddenly Ah kent what it wid have bin like for us. Ah'd have loved her always. A wid have made a life for us somehow, and Ah wid have made sure she had a' they chances Ah didnae get. She wid have made me strong, made me better too. Maybe Ah wid even have got to university yin day, somehow, an' got a dead good job.

Richt then, ah hated Rab. It bubbled up in me like a poison. He wis tae blame for a' o' this. Then Ah looked at Jessie an' saw her smilin' at me wi' his broon eyes. "The puir bugger's deid, and there's an end tae it," Ah telt Jessie, an' she wriggled in ma airms.

She's gettin' adopted soon- best thing, the social worker says, so she can get used to her new mum and dad while she's still wee.
 When she goes tae her new hame, Ah ken whit Ah'm ga'en tae dae. It'll soond daft tae ye, Ah ken, but Ah'm ga'en tae clear oot o' Dundee, an' ga'en up north an' see if Ah can find the red earth an sweepin' skies in 'Sunset Song'. Ah'll find a job until ma health finally braks doon, then Ah'm ga'en tae find a wee ,secret place, an auld ruined bothy and Ah'm ga'en tae tak' a' they pills Rab left ahind when he scarpered, an' Ah'm jist ga'en tae lie there lookin' at they clouds until the end.

No, ye must nae greet lik' that. Ah shouldnae hiv telt ye a' this, maybe. See A'll no see it, but whit maks me ok aboot it a' is that ma Jessie's ga'en tae get they chances.

An' maybe yin day when she's grown up, an' on a beach sometimes, an' hears a' they bloody gulls, an' sees a bairn wi' a balloon, she'll catch that wee, distant memory o' her ma that loved her.

The Woman Who Wrote Letters

Sheila woke as always with anger warming her thinning bones. In that brief moment between sleep and waking, she was free, blank, but whenever her eyes opened to the weak winter light, her brain moved into motion.
She remembered.
"I'll use the deckled cream writing paper today", she said out loud, pulling her rage around her like a familiar blanket.

Each day for 25 years, she had written a letter to her husband. Each night, she tore it up, her small hands briskly shredding the sides of paper and slinging them onto the fire.
Sometimes, in her saner moments, she considered the cost over the years of the writing paper. And of the cost to herself. How many hours of her life had she spent angrily writing, scribbling, when she could have been doing other things?

"Ann reeled him in, pulled him away from his family with her flashy clothes and red lipstick", Sheila told her sister Ruby regularly during the 25 years since that final night Jim came home and stayed only long enough to pack his things.
"I've brought those boys up single-handed. I never looked for a replacement father for them, because I'll never trust a man again", she said to Ruby, who murmured muted agreement.

She suffered. She stayed alone, as her few friends soon backed away, unable to deal with Sheila's incandescent anger. They listened uneasily for a while, then withdrew, making excuses not to be in touch. Even Ruby distanced herself.
"You need help, Sheila," she once said. "You need to talk to a counsellor and deal with this anger. Jim's behaved badly, but the boys need to see him more. You're doing everything possible to stop them seeing their dad."

Sheila leaned forward in her chair, fingers blanching tightly round the tea cup, about to speak, but Ruby held up her hand. "Listen to me, Sheila. Yes, you are staying, only just, within the agreed access arrangements but we all know you are making Jim's visits from the boys awkward or impossible… always some excuse like upset stomachs, school camp, football fixtures. You need to lighten up a bit, ease off. Go out, make new friends, and get your life back."

Sheila's face tightened up cold and hard, and she gripped the arm of her chair.

"Get out now," she told Ruby. "If you are siding with Jim, get out and stay away."

Sheila asked her sons never to tell her anything at all about their father's new life. Their round eyes were wide as they listened to her. "I don't want to know what's going on. He's wicked, and so is that woman he's with now." She never saw Jim again, but letters really had gone back and forward between them at first:
'How could you betray me?'
'I'm sorry.'

Eventually, Jim stopped getting her supermarket white envelopes with the matching sheets of paper inside, covered in her close, neat handwriting. Instead, brown envelopes arrived with typed sheets from her lawyer. Then, with the divorce finalised, these too stopped.
But habits are hard to break and in the lonely reaches of the early mornings or the bitter blackness of the winter nights Sheila wrote to him, the anger, hatred and disappointment pouring onto the pages. She never posted them. "I don't want a computer', she said to Ben when he showed her his laptop. 'I like pen and paper.'

The texture of her life felt uncomfortable, like wearing a knobbly hand-knitted jersey, or a rough tweed skirt next to the skin.
Some days her anger puttered weakly to a low gas. But other times it burned fierce and bright as she struggled with bills and juggled her work with raising the boys. As she stood freezing on Saturdays, watching her younger son run up and down a football pitch, she raged inwardly. She fretted as she hacked at a difficult shrub in the garden, her strength not quite equal to the task of culling the stiff wiry branches. A lick of clear, pure hatred ran through her body as she imagined her husband there, his strong arms snapping the cutters. That night, she wrote: "Why did you deceive and abandon me? Why were't you here with me today?"
In her head, each day, the hamster's wheel of rage rolled round.
"No doubt you are enjoying reinventing your youth, drinking champagne on sunlit holiday terraces next to that woman whose flesh is firm: she didn't give birth to your sons!" she silently shrieked at her absent husband.

Sheila finished today's letter and rose stiffly to her feet, aware of her aching head.

Jim Harrison woke early, a habit from his working days. He lay on his side, watching his wife sleep. Middle age had brought a slight puffiness to Ann's face, a blurring of her features. She snored faintly and as she moved in sleep, a frown gathered on her face.

He glanced at her bedside table and saw to his surprise, a Jane Austen. Usually she went in for chick lit or Mills and Boon. Must have been on television recently, he thought wryly.

He suddenly thought of his first wife. Sheila had been a keen reader, he remembered, but only of what she considered 'worthy' books. A cheap thriller or a magazine would have been a waste of time for her. That was some of the problem, there had been no lightness about her.

"She resents me still", he thought. His sons had awkwardly hinted as much on their very rare meetings with him when they were younger. He hadn't seen either of them for many years now, he thought sadly.

"Well, Sheila got her revenge, though she doesn't know it," he thought, wryly moving slightly away from his sleeping wife. He had expected a life of fun, travel, entertaining and socialising with his young second wife. Instead, to his dawning horror, he soon realized that what Ann wanted was children and a settled home. Twin girls were born within a year of their marriage.

He sighed, and wondered yet again why Sheila had never contacted him, never so much as dropped him a line or a Christmas card. He would have liked to have sometimes gone to the boys' school sports day or prize-giving with her.

"I could have taken the boys fishing, taught them to drive," he thought. "But Sheila just hauled up the drawbridge. Formal access only, the children dropped at my house by a friend or neighbour. Nothing from her…not even a letter asking for more maintenance!"

Jim sighed again, and lay back on the pillows. He'd made his choice all those years ago and now he had to live with it.

Ben arrived at the house first. He stood in his mother's kitchen, looking around. On the scrubbed pine table lay a pile of letters and papers. On the top was a gardening catalogue with an order form completed in Sheila's neat handwriting, but not sent. His eyes filled up again with tears.

He took off his jacket and the black tie and sat back down to deal with this first bundle of paperwork. His brother Simon would be along soon to help, but he could make a start, he thought.

Underneath the few bills and a postcard, he found a sheet of notepaper lying, folded over a matching envelope. It was written by his mother, to his father, and dated two weeks earlier.

Ben hunched at the table where he used to sit as a child, struggling with homework as his mother angrily banged the pots and muttered to herself. He could almost hear her:

"Why am I left with all this to do, and the car to service tomorrow, and how much is that going to cost?" The words had gone on, washing over him like a malevolent stream. He remembered his own small hand tensing, pushing down on the page until the pencil tip snapped...

He turned back to the letter.

"Dear Jim", it read. "I have been angry with you for so many years, it has become a habit. The resentment has taken me over and I shut down a big part of my life the day you walked out.
"I've written so many angry letters to you, and never sent them.
Recently, though, I've been having some health problems, and it has made me think about things afresh. Maybe I was a bit to blame for you leaving me, and maybe I could have moved on and found happiness with someone else if I'd wanted.
 "I'm not wanting contact with you – I can't go that far – but I need to drop this burden of anger I feel towards you, for my sake more than yours. So I'll be posting this letter to you.
"Regards, Sheila."

Ben looked out of the window at his mother's garden with its immaculate flower beds, and neat vegetable patch. He looked around the kitchen again, at the familiar cork pin board covered in notes, the battered old tea caddy he remembered as a child, the rack for saucepans.

He thought of all the school concerts and football matches his mother had watched on her own. His father had never once been there. He was a stranger, no part of his life.

"He never even took me fishing, never once saw me score a goal," Ben muttered in the empty kitchen.

Slowly, and with a blank, white face, he tore the letter into tiny pieces and dropped them in the wastebin.

Equal

In the night, owls winged silent
cats were lawless amongst tangled leaves.
Darkness closed us in, bringing rain.

In my midnight bed we scattered
pearls of desire in swooning sheets.

When you said 'I want you',
my bones were liquid with desire.
The elevator rushing through me
spoke to you, saying, 'I want you too.'

The wanting weighted even in scales
tipping us up to that equal place
which I never saw before
but always believed existed.

New Eyes

20-20 vision is hindsight
Intuition gives foresight.

Keratoconus caused my corneas
To falter, fade, slowly fail
Blighting my early manhood.

But then old Iris's death
- see, I know her name -
Gave me back sight.
Her car crash wreckage
her donor card
Swung my life round.

But now –

The bright supermarket shelves
Piled high with exotic fruit
I see overlaid by an old grocers' shop
With broken biscuit barrels
Sugar in blue twisted cones
And a man in a white apron
Stamping a ration book.

Now what I see with her eyes,
Is promiscuity, lack of respect
Where once I partied
Shagged, quaffed lager
Was Jack the lad.

Now I have vision to drive,
It is slowly, carefully.
I'm patient with the doddery,
the hesitant pedestrian
the flat-capped old man.

My mother thinks I'm nicer.

But best of all
now I really can
- and with crystal clarity -

See right through people.

Book Buddies

Kate shifted the weight of the shopping bags so that they were more evenly distributed across the top of Aaron's pushchair. She noticed that one of his gloves had fallen off and was lying, matted, on the apron of the buggy. The baby's face was mottled with the cold, and his cheeks were red and fiery.

"That'll be another tooth coming through," she said to him, as he crammed a whole fist into his mouth, strings of saliva threading down his coat. Kate sighed. She's best get him home out of the cold, and not stop by the library. She would make lunch, put him down for a nap and then it would be time to do the journey all over again, when they went back to collect Shelley from nursery.

She sighed again. TS Eliot had talked about life being measured out in coffee spoons, she vaguely remembered from a university lecture. Somehow, her life nowadays was now measured out in nappies, rusks, doses of baby painkillers and fish fingers.

She pushed the buggy towards their house. The house was new, convenient and completely lacking in character. When they first married, Kate and her husband Tom had had an old, cold flat with wonky floorboards, but they had moved to this new housing estate when Shelley was born.

"I hate this place," Kate muttered, pushing the buggy into the tiny hallway and unstrapping Aaron. She had wanted to call the baby Keats but Tom had vetoed it.

The trouble was that all her neighbours were nice, friendly and had young children.

But they had no books.

Instead, they had immaculate gardens, plastic containers for healthy breakfast cereals and tasteful ornaments. Kate knew that they secretly disapproved of her untidy house, and piles of paperbacks lying everywhere.

Later, she pushed the baby back into the school playground to wait for the bell signalling the end of Shelley's day at nursery. The baby dropped his glove onto the ground.

"Here you are, you need your gloves today," said a woman, handing back the glove.

She was around Kate's age, and holding onto the handle of a similar buggy. The shopping tray underneath the pram was crammed with books.

"Freezing, isn't it?" she said. "The Iceman Cometh right enough. I'm Diane, by the way, and this one in the buggy is Jupiter. Don't say it. Think I was still under the influence of the gas and air when I came up with that one, but it suits him. His brother's called Ronnie, boring, don't you think!"

A great weight rose up off Kate's shoulders and floated into the air. With sudden insight, she knew that Diane's house would be the one other in the estate where there were books spilling everywhere, and that her isolation was about to end.

Anticipation

Irene screws up her eyes against the hot, early sunshine, concentrating hard as she uses her clean yellow duster to buff up the ancient, brass handles of the town hall doors. Her short, iron-grey hair sits smoothly, her blue polyester overalls are trim and clean over her black trousers. In her overalls pocket crinkles a packet of cigarettes, nestling with a cheap lighter. Smoking. Her one vice, apart from the vodka, fresh orange and lemonade concoction she enjoys of a Saturday night at the bowling club with Walter, her husband of forty years.

Irene's huge spectacles magnify her surroundings, so that the dark - suited council officers scurrying past her up the stone steps look huge and blurry close-up, shoes big as boats as they thump away up towards the cool, dark panelled corridors. She smiles, contented. Each brass burnished, every desk dusted or bin emptied brings her nearer to her twin goals.

The first goal is her retirement, now five months away. She will hand in her security badge and leave work for the last time, no doubt laden with flowers and cards. Then she will no longer rise at five am, joints creaking, from the bed she shares with Walter, to begin her day's work. She will no longer endure the cold morning streets and the lumbering bus crowded with white and blanked-faced people, or the aching tiredness after a long morning sweeping and polishing.

Irene smiles again as she polishes the name plates, satisfied that every smear is obliterated. She works, but thinks ahead, anticipating a lie-in, a cup of tea and the newspaper as the world goes to work without her. Her wrinkled face, the smoker's legacy, creases happily once more, and she quietly hums Waltzing Matilda as she turns to the next task of this sweet May morning.

She sweeps the worn stone steps diligently. In her imagination, Irene sees a piggy bank filling as she works, a drip of money towards her goal. Very soon, the money will be saved for the tickets on Quantas flight 23871WG to Sydney, three weeks after she finishes work. As the Scottish sun glints sharply on Irene's spectacles, she imagines Ben and Michael, aged three and five, sporting sun hats, playing under hot Australian skies, watched by their laughing parents.

Irene frowns a little as she remembers the day Jill and her husband emigrated, how distraught she was but couldn't show it, how she resented friends talking about letters and emails and Skype. These things don't replace hugs and family sitting round the table at Christmastime. And in any case, what did she know about computers and such like?

Irene gathers up her brush and pan and tucks the duster in her pocket, smiling again. When she finishes her shift, she plans to go straight to the post office, to collect their passport forms. And tonight, while Walter dozes in front of the TV, she'll look out the airmail pad and envelopes and write the weekly letter to her daughter.

Night Patrol

Four lights out in Green Lane, that's not good. Dangerous. That's usually where I see the woman, where she runs to in the night. I've seen her tears, picked up by the street lights, glittering brightly on her white cheeks.

Once, I saw him.
"Get back here, you bitch!" he yelled, splashing through the dark, oily puddles. But she ran faster than him, her small feet barely touching the ground as she rushed through the empty streets. I had my hand on the passenger door that time, ready to open it, but she got away from him, off down a little alleyway.

"Jo, check out the west end in Southhaven tonight, up by the industrial estate. We've had a couple of complaints." The message, from Stan, my boss was on my work 'to do' list.

Lighting officer (night patrol), that's me. This is a strange, solitary job. I rarely see my colleagues as my working day begins around 10pm and ends at dawn.

"You're kinda like a vampire, aren't you?" said Mercy, my last girlfriend but one. She was from New York on a year's contract at the University. "A weird job, honey. You never get to see people!"

But, after what happened in Aberdeen, it suited me perfectly. I drive through the sleeping streets each night, patrolling, getting out now and then to walk around and noting faults with the street lighting, to report by email to Stan.

Sometimes there is a stray fox around, or a courting couple huddled in a doorway. A few drunks stagger around the streets, and there's the odd car about, but mostly it is just me and my smart phone.

"We really need a full upgrade in the Green Lane area," Stan emailed me after I'd noted frequent faults there. "But hey! like everything else, it's down to money, and the harbour area is the priority this year. Just do your best, kiddo!"

Stan called me kiddo, not because I was young-I'm 45- but as a way of being friendly. I could tell at the job interview that he just couldn't make me out.

"I've a degree in electrical engineering and a Masters in statistics," I told him.

The question hung in the air. Why the hell are you applying for this grade five post with the council, paying a third of what you could earn elsewhere? He asked the question differently.
"Well Jo, what attracts you to the job?"
I looked at him calmly.
"I want to work in a rural area so I can pursue my hobbies of bird watching and walking. Working nights gives me the chance to do these things during the day," I said. "And I own a cottage up the glens at Aberesk."

That answered his unspoken question as to how I could afford to live on the pay.

I liked the job, driving around at night. In the winter, I'd be finishing up as the gritting lorries started their morning battle to clear the roads. But the best bit was that I was miles and miles away from Aberdeen. From her. From all of that.

The woman was there again tonight. I glimpsed her first as I drove through the industrial estate. Her thin raincoat shimmered in the dusk, and her rain drizzled hair glistened faintly. Her feet seemed to barely touch the ground, she ran so fast through the dark, dank streets.

"Don't you run away from me, you fucking bitch! You whore!" He was in pursuit again, his rain darkened hair slicked against his head. His boots pounded and echoed along the street."Come fucking back here!" he roared with the rage of the inarticulate.

I'd been crawling along slowly, but now I put my foot down and reached her in seconds.
"Get in the car!" I yelled, flinging open the passenger door. She froze, then scrambled into the passenger seat.

I drove off fast, only saying: "Put on your seatbeat!"
Old habits die hard.

"Where are we going?" the woman asked after a few minutes. She shivered, and her teeth chattered slightly.

He had quickly disappeared from view. My last sight of him in the rear mirror was a huge fist upraised. Shaking at me.

"I live a few miles up towards Aberesk," I said. "You'll be safe there till we can sort something out."

I glimpsed her turning her face towards me. "But why?" Her voice tailed off. "I don't like bullies," I said abruptly, turning up the heating. I didn't like to see her shivering.

The weeks that followed were strange, even by my standards. We sat by the fire in my cottage during the day before I went to work, and Fiona told me her story. She'd married Ryan young, knowing that he had fiery temper, but thought she'd be able to cope with him.

"He was ok most of the time, but sometimes the smallest thing would set him off, " she said one day as we sat either side of the fire. "The way I put a new liner in the bin, or boiled potatoes, or chatted to the next door neighbour, anything could annoy him."

She looked at me sadly over her glasses. "Lucky we never had kids, they would have annoyed him too."

I fell half in love with Fiona. Only half, though. She was brave, uncomplaining, and feisty. But straight. So straight.

"I'm moving on, Stan".
It was rare for me to visit the office during the day, and he was surprised to see me.
I handed him the envelope with my month's notice in it.
"Where are you off to, then?" he asked.
"Going to Edinburgh, off to work for a big electronics company as product development manager."
"More money, I guess," said Stan wryly.
I held his gaze.
"Time to get back on with my life again," I said, giving him a tiny insight into my real private life for the first and last time.

The day I did the final packing up of the cottage, which sold remarkably fast, I found the old letter, stuck down the back of a chair, which Fiona had left me all those months ago. I re-read it, my eyes misting a little at her childish, rounded hand and use of lined notepaper. She thanked me for everything, for rescuing her, as she put it, and for helping her to find a new place to stay.

I crumpled up the letter and threw it on the dying embers of the final fire I'd lit to keep warm while I tidied round.

Fiona thought I'd been the heroine of the moment. Maybe I had been, a little.

But she opened up my eyes again, rolled away the boulder.

Let me finally put Aberdeen behind me, and start out again.

Memento Mori

I felt the deaths in Montparnasse.
Crushed lilies, sickeningly sweet
Slump on marble slabs.

A man's face stares out
Set in stone, smile frozen
Bespectacled, hair neat forever
Shrouded by faded tulips

I thrust bright red roses
A cheerfulness of carnations
Into my mother's arms
While she lives to enjoy them.

Beginning

Susan scurried along the crowded corridor and out of the office block into the shimmering dampness. Her pony tail, too young for her, swung irritatingly, her tiny glittering hair clasps betraying her small vanities.

At the bus stop, she opened her bag, which held anti-depressants in a sealed packet, a single tweed button from a man's jacket and a chemist's paper bag, sellotaped. She took out her old, pink purse with the zip which tugged —a 21st birthday present, the leather now worn and faded— and removed the coins for the fare.

The bus jolted forward through the glistening, rainy streets and moved out into the countryside towards her village. Her gaze looked out across the rain-smeared countryside and suddenly alert, she spotted the woodland-fringed field where she had met him that last night, all those weeks ago. She remembered his unshaven face, with its tiny, fair bristles glinting in the watery moonlight, and the rough, knobbled texture of his jacket under her.

That was before he went away, back to Aberdeen, back to his wife and children.

In a trance, she unlocked the drab green front door and went straight to the bathroom, with its bottles lining the bathtub and the pink knitted toilet roll cover which had been her mother's before she went into the home.

Susan removed the paper bag and slowly unwrapped the pregnancy test kit.

Minutes later, she watched as the thin blue line brightened, strengthened, telling her what she wanted to know. Still holding the small plastic tube, she gazed at the result, watching the future begin at last, and seeing her loneliness retreat.

The Retail Intoxication Syndrome

I'm sitting at the disco, nursing the second and final bottle of beer of the evening.

No point in adding drink dependency to everything else...

The dance floor bounces and springs in time to the beat as women have fun. Usually my favourite things, boogie nights, where heat and good-time music and laughter merge, and the camaraderie of the women reminds you what it's all about.

But I'm distracted. I'm musing on the Retail Intoxication Syndrome and wondering why we- even the most savvy and smart of us- succumb to it every time? Maybe there's an immunisation we can have, like a 'flu jab, to protect us, so we can just enjoy the shopping without the other bit kicking in?

We all know where we like to go. I love it. Apart from having fun buying the bags of tealights, the flat pack bookcases and the picture frames, you can watch families with kids actually enjoying the visiting to the children's furniture and toys bit. All good stuff.

But just look more closely and you'll spot them. The pair of women circling the soft furnishings section, picking up a bathmat here and a duvet cover there. They exchange glances of delight as, moving onwards, they reach simultaneously for the same desk lamp. Their trolley piles with goodies, and is it hers or hers they are buying?

Their fate is sealed over the meatballs they have in the café, and the shared cheesecake (two forks, half each). Suddenly, although they've only known each other a few weeks, it is all wonderful. They have already discovered that they both like old black and white films, holidaying in Skye in the pouring rain and love cats, not dogs. They know that they both like Jackie Kay's poetry and hate the soaps. And now here they are, giggling as they try out beds and sit in comfy chairs. They are in perfect accord.

You just know what is going to happen next. They'll shoehorn into one flat together and merge their books, house plants and pets.

The pants pose a problem, because they take the same size and of course, they like the same kind. With joy at such an easy answer to this dilemma, they cut the labels off one set of knickers: hey presto, all is well again!

And they snuggle close at night listening to the rain and the wind blow, and feel safe and happy.

And it would be wonderful if that was it, the happy ending for ever and a day, which it is for some, of course. Marriages made in retail heaven.

But unfortunately it doesn't always work. Future shopping trips see this couple sitting grim faced as food congeals while they argue about the things all couples argue about, but just more so, because there's more at stake– the washing up bowl with dirty water left in it, the penchant for Strictly, the dislike of Strictly, money, ironing– and so it all unravels.

I sip the beer. There's a woman looking at me across the room, holding my gaze as she moves slightly to the tempo of the music.

She's curvy, mature, sexy, lovely white teeth, silk shirt, smile friendly but not too intense. And she's holding a bottle of beer which is the same brand as mine.

I can just predict it all, with hideous clarity.

The voice inside my head and gut says no, and for once I listen.
I finish my drink and head off into the lonely night, where a baleful orange moon hangs reproachfully in the sky and watches my solitary progress home.

I'll be shopping online for the new coffee table.

Unless, of course, that curvy lady with the silk shirt ,who slipped her phone number into my jeans pocket as I left the disco, wants a trip to come and help me choose it...

TV Dinner at Edinburgh Zoo

Fresh leaves cushioning his bones
The wise ape reaches for his tv snack-
carrots, shredded cabbage, a few choice grapes.
His fingers rummage slowly in the bowl. He sighs.

Afternoon entertainment. Here it comes.

Scots, pale winter faces freckle-dusted,
Their blue eyes set under shining red hair,
Parade before him, chattering.

His wire mesh barrier keeps out
narrow-eyed children with sticky lollies.
How inappropriate their comments, he muses
looking fondly at his own children
playing quietly, scampering, grooming.

He watches a child staring rudely
Her tongue stuck out, scowling,
Miss Kitty bag sliding off her shoulder.

Boring girl, and needs a good scrub, he thinks.
Not good viewing today.

Nearby, a white-faced Saki monkey shrieks to him:
"Weekend might be better, more tourists!"

The wise ape sighs again,
Scooping up the last apple slices,
Rearranging his leaves, settling for a nap.

Dawn

In the early morning, you slipped
fast and warm from my bed, my love
still wrapping round you.

You drove quiet through darkling streets
lamplight puncturing the velvet skies
till, moving swift and sure, you saw
the first shard of morning
slip through the blackness
as dawn slid slow into the sky.

The mackerel of a Scottish summer sky
with pink hint of a good day
was broken

suddenly

by shaft of weak sun,
glistening the trees, the cars,
picking out the fox, as he scurried
fast and furtive, hurrying
away from the light, back to shadows.

Then you were home again
in beloved Edinburgh
with sun bathing dear cobbles

And all was right with the world.

Into the Light

With the passing of days, where weeks
idle down to months, to changing seasons,
there is the moving down the road
forwards towards the blazing beacon.

Fuelled by rising happiness
my feet move onwards, spirits lifting.
Sunshine moves its tendrils round me
warming me back to life, restoring.

A tree root catches now and then
Or a stone needs pulled from shoe
Minor setbacks to progress,
To be expected.

I now walk joyous, free
untramelled, released,
past glistening hedgerows, shining waters,
by birds and bees and butterflies
through cobbled streets filled with
music and laughter and words
amid the friendship of coffee cups.

Held by and holding your hand
now and always, now and forever
knowing this is now truly forever,
I walk steadily, assured,

Into the light.